ROLL CALL

THE STORY OF
NOAH'S ARK
&
THE WORLD'S FIRST LOSERS

WORDS BY
JOHN GOLDTHWAITE
PICTURES BY
HENRI GALERON

A Harlin Quist Book

Published by Harlin Quist, Incorporated
Library of Congress Catalog Card: 78-70570
ISBN: 0-8252-7481-8 for the paperback
and 0-8252-7482-6 for the hardcover
Text copyright © 1978 by John Goldthwaite
Pictures copyright © 1978 by Henri Galeron
First printing
Printed in the U.S.A.

**There goes old Noah,
And there goes his yacht,
Three cheers for the creatures
That Noah forgot.**

Noah forgot to invite the Avote,
Who had to go swimming for want of a boat.

The Ark sailed away with no Binikin Bot ;
That creature's washed up because Noah forgot.

The Crumble they sped to the docks in a cart,
But they bounced him too hard and the beast fell apart.

The Dibbit inflated the pouch in his cheeks,
Which kept him afloat for a number of weeks !

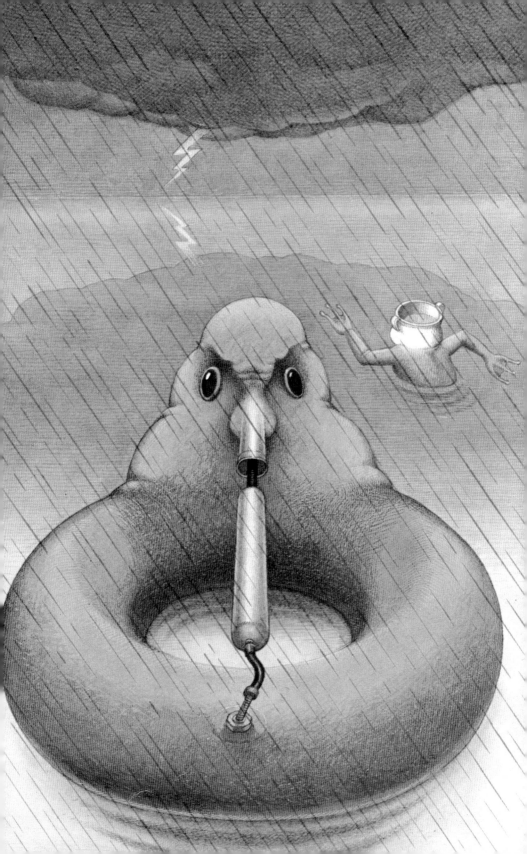

The Egg in its haste to the Ark gave a wobble ;
Its yolk went to waste on a street made of cobble.

Noah looked forward to greeting the Fum,
But the frivolous beast had forgotten to come.

The Gullet, exhausted, lay down on a lawn,
And drowned in the rain in the midst of a yawn.

The Hilly regarded the flood as a hoax,
He would not go sailing with sensible folks ;
And the Hogey who could not make up his own mind,
The Hilly talked into remaining behind.

The Ark in exactly six days was to sail,
And the Ick had been sentenced to seven in jail.

The Jollijo boated away on a wave
In a cabinet drawer, looking terribly brave.

In the last-minute rush to go sailing, the Krass
Jumped over a Krip, and fell down a crevasse.

The Lollaway scolded her pillow and wept;
Old Noah had sailed while that bird overslept.

Beware of the Flood, said a note to the Meech,
But the Meech had gone swimming that day at the beach;
And the note never came, for the silly Moleet
Had dropped it while pecking for bugs in the street.

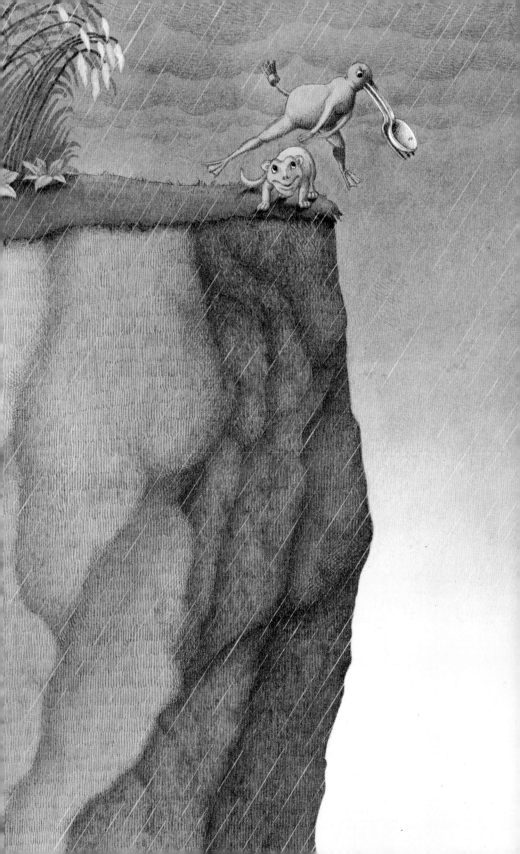

Unfit for the sail, in a local saloon
Dead drunk were the Noise and the Nollypatoon

O was the Ozimandozimandoa
Who pooh-poohed a sail with that silly old Noah.

P was the Pugly, who circled confused
In the torrent of rain, and must now be excused.

The two-headed Q-dilly-Q in the roar
Of the rain was engaged in a fierce tug-of-war :
Which way was the Ark, to the west or the east ?
The heads disagreed ; now the heads are deceased.

The Reeber, while running, fell flat on his face.
Now who would go sailing with such a disgrace ?

A tidal wave scuttled the staggering Shag
As he nibbled on sandwiches packed in a bag.

**The Twistle stayed home, for she thought it was best,
And she drowned bailing rainwater out of her nest.**

**The Upsy arrived with a marvelous leap,
And bounced off the deck and went down in the deep.**

**We sail two by two, Noah said, but the Vex
Stayed ashore for the want of an opposite sex.**

**Bad luck for the Wibble, who had to collide
With a left-over Weasel thrown over the side.**

Thirty miles to the ship! cried the brave little Xot,
And he shouldered his bag and set out at a trot;
But he wasn't, you see, but the size of a dot,
And a yard and a half was as far as he got.

The Yit punched the Yellow Yafoo in the nose,
The Yellow Yafoo stomped the Yinglebird's toes;
The Yelp and the Yoyocat hollered and wailed,
And as they all battled, away the Ark sailed.